Maths BASICS

FOR AGES 3-4 PRE-SCHOOL

Contents

How to use this book

Numeracy Basics helps you to help your child practise many important basic skills covered in the *National Numeracy Strategy* and *National Curriculum*.

Each book is divided into *30 units* of work which focus on *one clear* objective.

Most of the units are designed using the same easy-to-follow *key features*. In some cases these features are combined into one activity, offering further practice where appropriate.

Title
Target learning objective.

Look and learn
Introduces and explains the target objective. Provides an example to illustrate it.

Practice
Provides straightforward practice activities based on the target objective.

Challenge
Provides activities to extend and challenge.

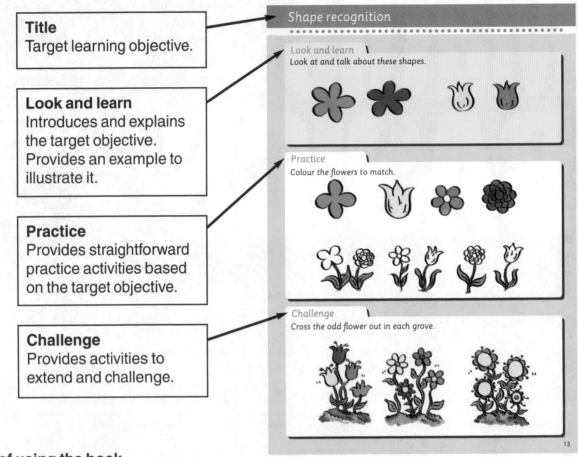

Suggested way of using the book

- It is suggested that your child works systematically through the book.

- Try tackling one unit per week.

- Read through and discuss the *Look and learn* section with your child to make sure the key objective is understood.

- Help your child get started on the Practice section.

- After this, your child can start to work fairly independently through the page, but will need further support and encouragement.

- The answers are supplied at the end of the book for checking each unit on its completion.

Enjoy the book!

Look, learn and practice

What is in the parcels? Join each parcel to the correct present.

Look, learn and practice

Join the pairs with a line.

Look, learn and practice

Join the pairs of objects which belong together with a line.

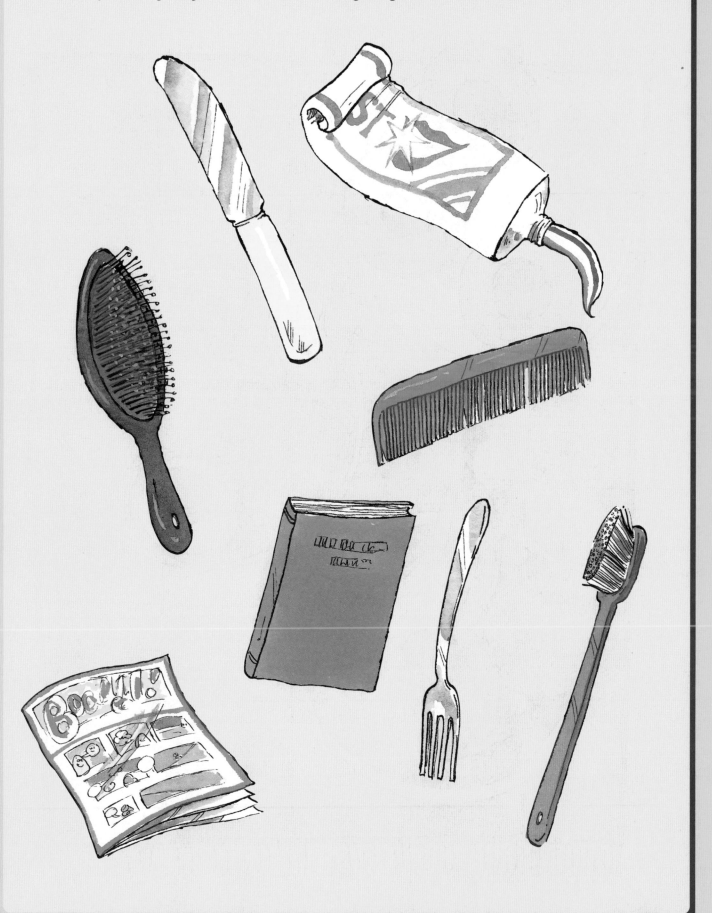

Look, learn and practice

Talk about the odd shape out on each plate.

Look, learn and practice

Find the objects in the cupboard that match those left out.

Look, learn and practice

Talk about the picture. Look for the spots, stripes, round and square shapes.

spots   stripes   round things   square things

Matching shapes

Look, learn and practice

Talk about these objects. Find and match the pairs.

Look, learn and practice

Colour the lids to match the boxes.

Look, learn and practice

Talk about the differences in these two pictures.

Look and learn

Find your way through this maze. Collect the ball and the teddy bear on your way.

Shape recognition

Look and learn

Look at and talk about these shapes.

Practice

Colour the flowers to match.

Challenge

Cross the odd flower out in each grove.

1

Look and learn

Talk about the number one.

  1 one 1

Practice

Colour the cakes which have **1** candle.

Challenge

Find the groups of one. Join them to the **1**.

1

Look and learn

Talk about the number two.

  2 two

Practice

Colour the pots which have **2** flowers in them.

Challenge

Find the groups of two. Join them to the 2.

Look and learn

Talk about the number three.

3 three 3

Practice

Colour the plates which have **3** buns on them.

Challenge

Find the groups which have three. Join them to the 3.

Patterns

Look and learn

Look at these patterns. Finish them off.

Practice

Join each animal to its home. Follow the pattern.

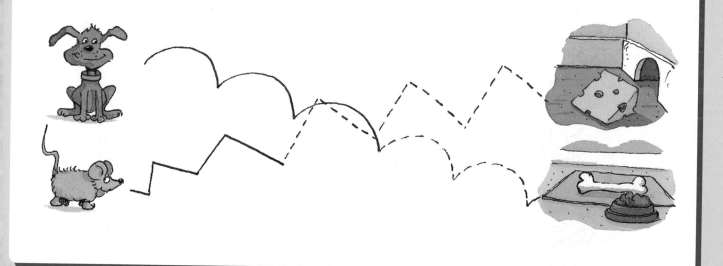

Challenge

Continue each pattern.

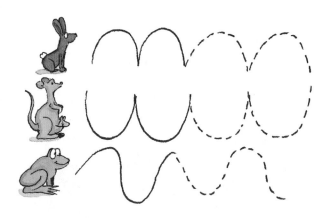

Look and learn

Talk about the number four.

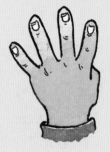  4 four 4

Practice

Colour the dogs which have **4** spots on them.

Challenge

Find the groups which have four. Join them to the 4.

Look and learn

Talk about the number five.

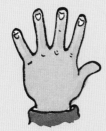  5 five

Practice

Colour the cards which have **5** things on them.

Challenge

Find the groups which have five. Join them to the 5.

Measures

Look and learn

This is long:

This is short:

Practice

Draw a long tail.

Draw a short tail.

Draw long whiskers.

Draw short whiskers.

Challenge

Draw a short collar on a short dog.

Draw a long collar on a long dog.

Look and learn

Talk about the number six.

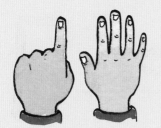  6 six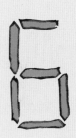

Practice

Colour **6** red apples on each tree.

Challenge

Find the groups which have six. Join them to the 6.

Look and learn

Talk about the number seven.

Practice

Circle the bowls with **7** fish in them.

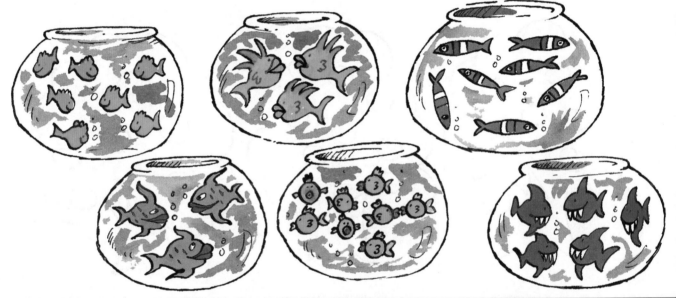

Challenge

Draw **7** spots on each fish.

Shape recognition

Look and learn

Look at and talk about these shapes.

Practice

Join each person to their shadow.

Challenge

Where does each shape fit?

23

Look and learn

Talk about the number eight.

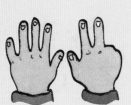 8 eight

Practice

Colour the snakes with **8** spots.

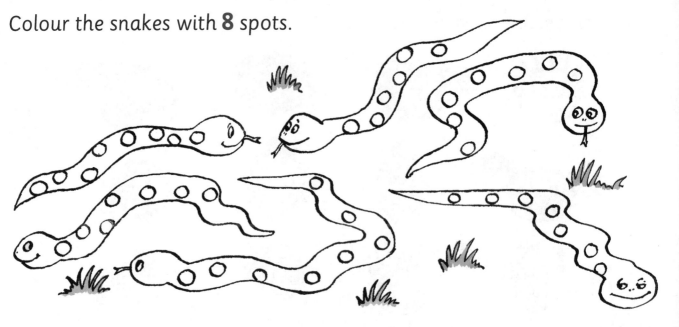

Challenge

Draw **8** spots on each snake.

Look and learn

Talk about the number nine.

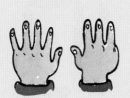  9 nine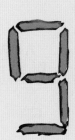

Practice

Draw **9** holes in the leaf.

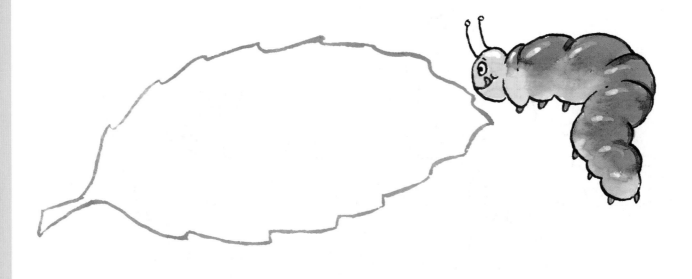

Challenge

Join **9** to its home.

Look and learn

Talk about the number ten.

Practice

Colour the sandcastles which have **10** flags on them.

Challenge

Join the number **10** to its home.

All about 0

Look and learn

Talk about the number zero.

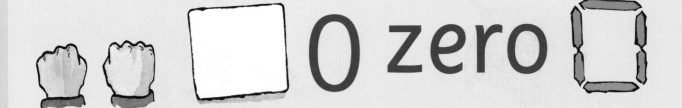

0 zero

Practice

Colour the plates that have nothing on them.

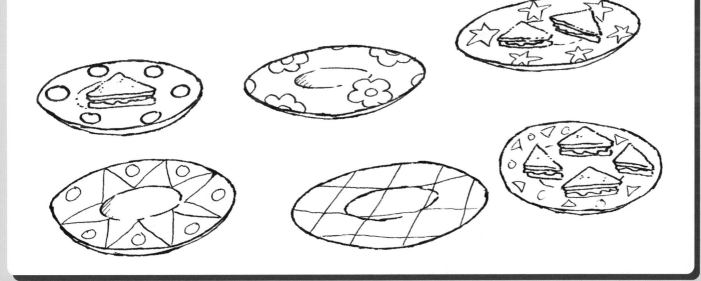

Challenge

Find the empty boxes. Join them to the 0.

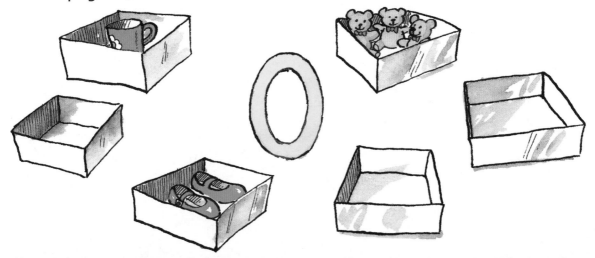

One more

Look and learn

Talk about 'one more' with your child by counting the ladybirds.

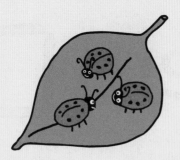

One more

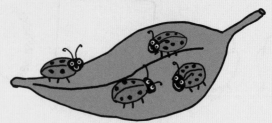

Practice

Draw **one more**. Count how many that makes.

Challenge

Draw holes on each leaf to show **one more**.

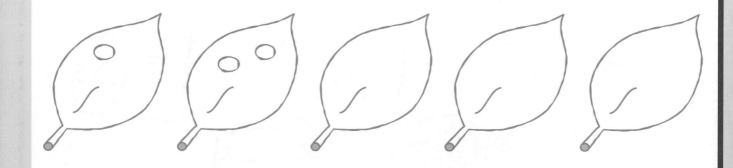

Recognising numbers

Look and learn

Look at and talk about these numbers.

 1 2  3  4 5

Practice

Colour the balloons to match the number colours above.

Challenge

Cross the odd one out.

1	X	•	* *	♥	◆
2	XX	• •	***	♥ ♥	◆ ◆
3	XX	• • •	***	♥ ♥	◆ ◆ ◆
4	XX XX	• • • •	***	♥ ♥ ♥ ♥	◆ ◆ ◆ ◆

Look and learn

Remind your child of the numbers 1 to 3.

Practice

Join the matching teddies.

Challenge

Colour the odd one out.

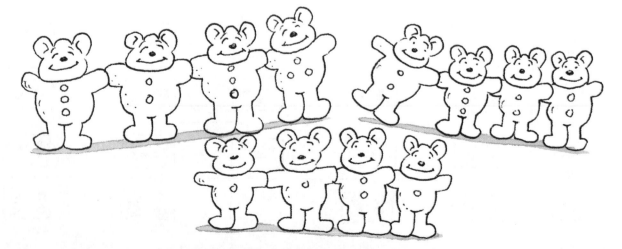

Counting to 5

Look and learn

Count and say the numbers out loud.

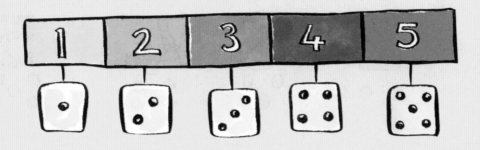

Practice

Join the fingers to the correct number on the number lines.

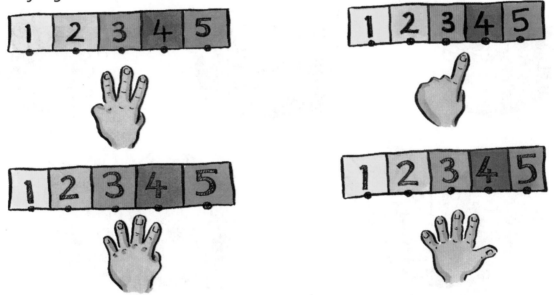

Challenge

Find the bags with the same number of marbles. Join them with a line.

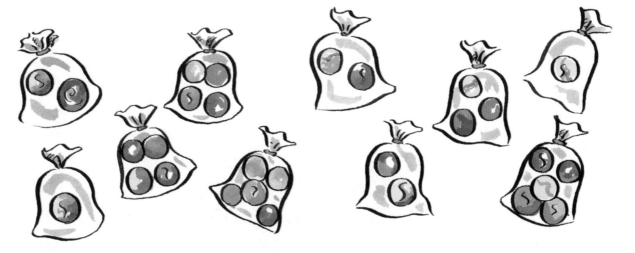

Look and learn

Look again at the numbers 1 to 5.

Practice

Count the chicks. Write how many there are.

Challenge

Draw some eggs in each nest. Count how many there are.